LIFE WITHOUT THE BABY

JOURNAL

by

Emily R. Long

Life Without the Baby Journal © 2017 Emily R. Long.

Printed in the United States of America
First Printing 2017

ISBN: 978-0-9965556-6-1

Firefly Grace Publishing
Burlington, VT 05403
www.EmilyRLong.com

Interior and Cover Design: ShiftFWD
Author Photo: Greeta Soderholm

Other Available Books by Emily:

Invisible Mothers: When Love Doesn't Die (September 2015)

You Are Not Alone: Love Letters from Loss Mom to Loss Mom (April 2016)

From Father to Father: Letters from Loss Dad to Loss Dad (November 2016)

Life Without
the Baby Journal:
Redefining
Life, Self, and
Motherhood After
Loss

In Gratitude and Honor

This book is dedicated to all the mothers I've come to know
on this journey of life after loss:

The world may call you bereaved,
but grief is just one small piece of your motherhood.

The love and devotion you have for your children
is a far, far better descriptor of the mother that you are.

I have seen you in the depths of grief.
I have watched you rise.
I have witnessed you lift each other up.

Loss and grief are what happened to you.
But your love is a force of nature,
Your love is who you are.

You are a beautiful mother.

I am grateful to know you.

xoxo

In loving memory of Ginny.
My friend and fellow lover of books and words and learning.
You will always inspire me.
I miss you.

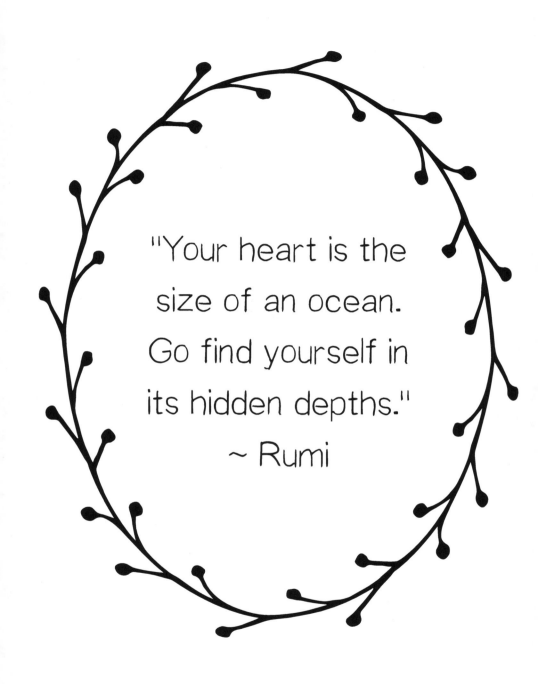

"Your heart is the
size of an ocean.
Go find yourself in
its hidden depths."
~ Rumi

Hi Beautiful Mama,

I am both excited for you to join me on this journey of redefining life and self after loss and terribly sorry that we are meeting here.

This journey of life after loss can feel incredibly lonely and confusing. Trying to make sense of the world and ourselves after our babies die can feel overwhelming and chaotic. Getting out of bed may take everything we have. Trying to function in normal life can feel like more than we can endure. Nothing makes sense and life feels, well, just plain wrong.

When our baby dies we don't just lose our baby, we also lose our sense of identity and sense of self. We are left questioning:

> *Without my babies, who am I?*
> *How do I make sense of life now that my baby is gone?*
> *What do I do with my life without a baby to raise?*
> *Will I ever be the person I used to be again?*

This identity loss after our babies die isn't something that is often discussed. A significant deal of attention is given to grieving our babies, how much we miss them, and coping with the chaos of grief in general. However, little is said about the loss of identity and struggle to figure out who **we** are in this life after loss.

And that's unfortunate, because learning to redefine life and reclaiming a new sense of who we are is an essential piece to finding light and joy and peace again after this devastating loss.

That is what this journal is all about.

Self-rediscovery.
Deciding who we want to be and how to be that person.
Grieving the old us, the pieces of who we were that died with our baby.
Integrating pieces of who we were and who we want to be to create who we are now.

Redefining life and what it means for us now.
Getting clear on what we want from life now and stepping forward into that.
Making meaning out of our experiences of love and loss.

We don't get a choice when our babies die. We are thrust into this world of grief and loss without warning or agreement. In a moment, everything changes and, suddenly, here we are in life without our babies.

The sense of powerlessness, helplessness, and devastation when we can't save our babies fucking sucks.

We do, however, get a choice about who to be and what we want life to mean after the life we expected crumbles under us.

I won't lie. It's not an easy road to navigate and it asks a tremendous amount from us.

This path asks us to learn to live in the gray of life:

To live and to grieve.
To allow for joy and for sadness.
To love and to lose.
To fight and to surrender.
To love who we were and to love who we are now.
To forgive ourselves and to forgive life.

I will never tell you that this path to redefining life, motherhood, and self after the loss of our babies is easy or smooth.

It's not. It's bumpy and rocky and painful.

It's also, as the clique goes, absolutely worth it.

In a nutshell, this is what I will ask you do to on this journey:

Love yourself as much as you love your baby.
Fight for yourself as hard as you fought for your baby.

You deserve that.

Most of the work in this book will be self-reflection and "homework" that you do on your own.

There is, however, also a Facebook group in which I hope you will connect to share your discoveries, challenges, successes, and more with me and with others moving through this process. The group is where you can ask for clarification, request help and support, cry when you need to, and laugh when you can.

Come find us on Facebook at https://www.facebook.com/groups/LifeWithoutTheBaby/and request to join :)

Our journey is uniquely our own, yet we're still all in this together.

Let's get started!

"Hold the Vision,
Trust the Process."
~ author unknown

Chances are, if you've chosen to purchase this journal, you've asked yourself some or all of these questions:

Will I ever feel normal again?
Is it possible to feel truly happy again?
Will I ever feel fulfilled again?
Will my life have a sense of purpose again?
Will I ever feel passionate about anything again?
Who am I if I'm not a (typical) mother? AM I still a mother?

These are the questions I have heard over and over again from clients, from fellow moms in loss groups, and from friends struggling with the death of their children.

When we lose our baby, our entire sense of self and perception of life can completely crumble underneath us. Life as we know it isn't just turned upside down – it's demolished. Flattened, swept away, and emptied like a desolate landscape, barren of life.

Life will never be the same again. We will never be the same again.

However, my answer to those questions is unequivocally YES. This I know without a doubt.

You can feel a sense of normal again.
You can be truly and deeply happy and joyful again.
You can feel fulfilled again.
You can feel a sense of purpose in life again.
You can feel passionate again.
You can redefine yourself and have a solid sense of identity again, one that includes the mother that you are.

You will never be the same you again, but you can be happy and fulfilled as the new you. You can find a sense of familiarity and comfort in who you are as the new you.

I can't give you all the answers to finding joy and beauty and purpose in the new you and the new life you have – but I can give you the tools and the questions to ask to find your own answers.

My intention is that this journal helps you answer another common question:

Where do I go from here?

This journal will give you many things to think about and new questions to consider. I will be asking you to stretch and get a little uncomfortable. You probably won't like some of the things I ask you to consider. It will take dedicated time and attention if you want to see shifts and changes for yourself.

To get the most out of this journal, I would recommend setting aside scheduled, commited time to be with yourself, to consider the questions and assignments I present to you, and to seek your answers in yourself.

Make yourself a cozy, quiet space in which to do this work. Find a candle in your favorite scent. Get yourself a special pen or pencil to use in this journal. Settle in with a cup of your favorite tea or coffee or hot cocoa. Perhaps keep some tissues at hand because this isn't easy work. Tears seem to be an inevitable part of the process

Your first mini assignment:
Set an intention for this work.

Create your cozy space and pull out your special pen or pencil and settle in the take some time with yourself.

Set your intention for this doing the work in this journal.

Don't force an intention or an expectation for this work, simply let these questions roll around in your mind and heart and see what shows up.

"How much can I reasonably expect to invest in terms of time and energy to this process?"
"What do I want to get out of this journal?"
"How do I want to feel at the end of this journal?"
"What questions am I hoping will be answered by this journaling process?"

Reflect on those questions and set an intention for what you want to get out of this journal and our time together.

Then, bring it to the Facebook group and let us support you in that intention! Come introduce yourself and get to know others on this journey.

We are all in this together.

Mini Assignment 1: Set an intention for this work.

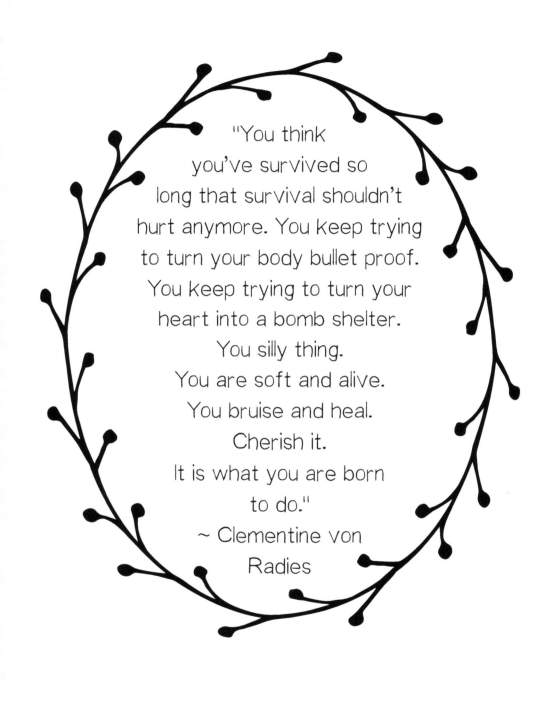

"You think
you've survived so
long that survival shouldn't
hurt anymore. You keep trying
to turn your body bullet proof.
You keep trying to turn your
heart into a bomb shelter.
You silly thing.
You are soft and alive.
You bruise and heal.
Cherish it.
It is what you are born
to do."
~ Clementine von
Radies

As much as it pains me to say this – the first essential piece to redefining and creating a new life after loss is to say another good-bye.

When our babies die, it's obvious that we grieve for them. We can't help but grieve and mourn for them and for the unfairness of having to say good-bye before we've really had a chance to say hello.

There is a lot of talk and encouragement in the baby loss communities and grief world to memorialize and honor our babies. There are countless discussions of how to celebrate them and their too-brief lives. We are encouraged to engage in rituals of mourning and good-bye.

What isn't often discussed is the importance of saying good-bye to the person we were before our baby died and the mother we expected to be with them.

There is little conversation about or awareness of the need to grieve and honor the woman we were or the mother we were supposed to be. We are rarely encouraged to celebrate our former selves or to engage in rituals to say good-bye to the women we were pre-loss.

The truth is who we were and the mother we would have been died along with our baby. The moment our baby died or was given a terminal diagnosis, we became someone new.

The old you is gone forever.
The non-bereaved mother you expected to be will never be.

You didn't ask to be this new person. You didn't ask to be this kind of mother – a mother without her child to hold. It's not fair on any level.

In order to embrace the new person that you are, however unfairly she came to be, you have to say good-bye to the former you and the would-have-been you.

Both deserve to be mourned and grieved for as much as your baby does.

Obviously, grieving ourselves is going to take as time – as all grief does. Even 13+ years after the death of my first daughter, I still at times grieve for the mother I might have been and ache for pieces of the woman I was.

As you work through the chapters of this book, these pieces will be something you visit and revisit, circle through and back again over and over. Saying good-bye and saying hello is a continuous process.

Life is a continuous journey of hello and goodbye.

What I'm offering here are tools and questions and perspectives you can pull out over and over again as needed on your individual journey.

Your Assignment:
Say Good-bye to the Former You

Create a ritual.

Rituals can a valuable part of saying good-bye. That's why funerals and memorials are so pervasive and common. As humans, we have a need to carve out time and space to remember, to say good-bye, to honor and to mourn those we love.

When I realized I needed to say good-bye and grieve for the person I was before my daughters died and for the mother I expected to be to them, I held a private ritual. I bought a bouquet of wildflowers and gathered up a burning bowl, a copy of an old picture of myself, a symbol of the mother I wanted to be, a notebook and pencil, a candle and matches.

I took it all to a creek near my home and sat on the shore by the water. I lit the candle in the burning bowl and spread the other items around me.

Then I took a page from the notebook and tore into scraps of paper. On each scrap, I wrote what I loved and missed about who I used to be. I honored all the pieces of myself that had died with my daughters. I also acknowledged all the pieces of myself I wasn't quite so sad to say good-bye to, the pieces of myself that, looking back, weren't things I particularly liked about myself.

One by one, I lit them with the candle and dropped them into the bowl to burn away. (In recent years, I've found for burning bowl rituals such as this, tissue paper burns much easier than notebook paper!)

Next, I took the copy of my picture and also touched it to the flame and allowed it to burn in the bowl. While it did, I pulled the notebook back out and wrote a sort of eulogy to the person I had been.

I honored her. Remembered her. Noted her accomplishments and her failures. I wrote about her flaws and her strengths. I noted all the dreams and plans she had had for her life. I wrote about all that I loved about her and all that I would miss about being her.

And then I let those pages burn away as well.

When that was complete, I blew out the candle and removed it from the burning bowl. In the bowl I placed my symbol of motherhood and the bouquet of wildflowers.

To finish the ritual, I walked into the water a few feet and slowly dipped the bowl beneath the rushing water of the creek. I let water fill it and swirl through it until it had swept away the flowers, the dandelion, and the ashes of who I had been and I watched it all disappear downstream.

Of course, I cried through the entire thing. But I felt lighter and clearer after completing my ritual.

I still missed who I had been. I still longed for the motherhood I had planned. But I felt lighter and somehow cleaner. It felt good to honor and acknowledge the woman I had been and the mother I would have been.

So, that is your assignment. Create a ritual of good-bye. Perhaps you do a ritual similar to mine or create something entirely different. (Time of year and location alone may greatly effect your ability to replicate my ritual!)

Maybe you do yours alone as I did or perhaps you gather a circle of trusted friends and ask them to participate with you.

Maybe yours is simpler than mine. Perhaps it's more complex.

Whatever feels good and right for you to say good-bye, do that.

Do something.

You deserve that acknowledgement and honoring too.

If you get stuck or aren't sure how to go forward, bring it to the Facebook group and let us help. Or just come and share what you did and how it was for you.

As always, we're all in this together.

Your Assignment: Say Good-bye to the Former You

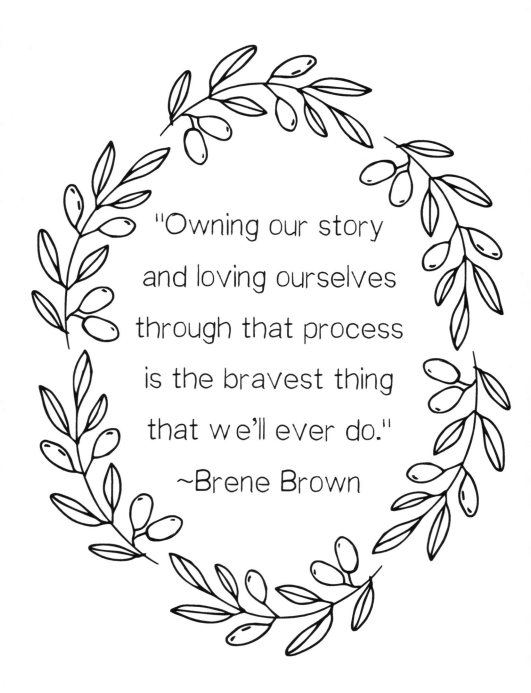

"Owning our story
and loving ourselves
through that process
is the bravest thing
that we'll ever do."
~Brene Brown

We have one more good-bye to recognize and say on this journey.

When we get pregnant and prepare to bring our child into this world, we expect that life will change. We willingly choose to have our life change in drastic and profound ways. We are ready and willing to claim the role and title of "mother."

Then our baby dies.

Our life and our world *does* change profoundly and drastically.

Life changes in ways we never could have expected and in ways we never would have chosen. Life changes, but definitely not in the way we had planned.

However, as we often neglect the need to grieve for who we were and the mother we would have been, we rarely give ourselves permission to truly say good-bye and grieve the life we planned to have with our baby.

We planned to change our lives for our children. Change did happened. We get a new life, but definitely not the one we joyfully anticipated.

Now we have to create a new life out of the mess of the one we were handed.

The new life you create may or may not ever include a baby. That uncertainty is often one of the most painful parts of saying good-bye to the life we planned – and often the reason we resist saying good-bye to that expected life.

The hard truth is that even if we do have another baby (before or after the baby who died) and get the have those aspects of the life we planned – parenting, sweet baby scents, watching them grow and learn – it still won't be the same life we expected to have as parents. The innocence of life before loss is gone and will never be for us again.

That innocence and simple trust in life is perhaps one of the things we grieve most deeply when the life we planned is taken from us.

Therefore, much like honoring and acknowledging the person we used to be and the mother we would have been, we must also honor and acknowledge the life we planned to have with our children.

Your Assignment:
Say Good-Bye to the Life You Had Planned

Like your last assignment, create some kind of ritual to say good-bye and release the life you had planned to live.

You can structure it similar to your last one or create something completely new.

Here are some elements to consider including:

- A good-bye letter
- Acknowledging:
    o What you loved about the life you planned
    o What you will miss about it
    o What about that life you are happy to leave behind
    o What elements of that life you will bring with you into this life you have
- A symbol of that life
- A symbol of what you are taking from that life and bringing with you into your current and future life

Take your time creating this ritual. And at the same time, try not to over think it. Simply do what you feel moved to do.

Again, if you feel stuck or stymied in any way, bring it to the group! We'll help you get things flowing.

Also come to share how the experience was for you. None of this has to be done without support.

Because, as always, we're all in this together.

Your Assignment:
Say Good-Bye to the Life You Had Planned

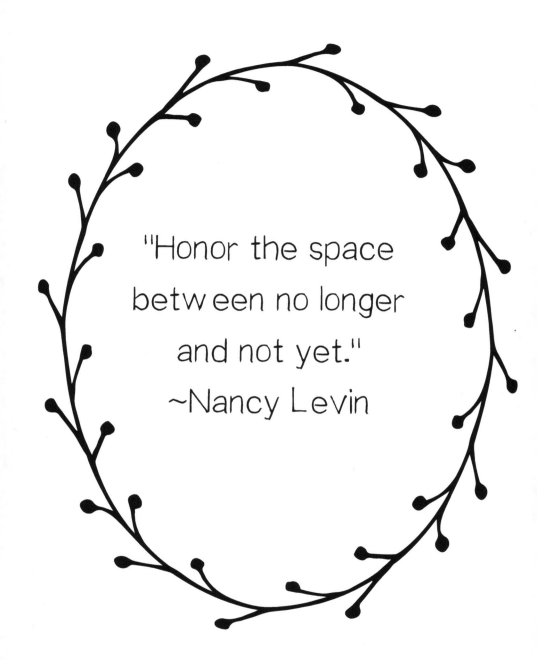

"Honor the space
between no longer
and not yet."
~Nancy Levin

You are living in what I call "The In-Between."

It's a space where life has undeniably changed. You are no longer who you used to be and aren't yet who you will be. Life isn't what it was and it's not yet what it will be.

The gap. The gray. The space between the monkey bars.

The In-Between.

It's an unsettling place to be because nothing feels solid or steady. It's like living through the aftershocks of an earthquake – the worst appears to be over yet the earth beneath you is still shaking and shifting at unpredictable moments.

You have survived, but may be fearful and uncertain about what could come next. What comes next might be the thing that brings you down completely.

You have a foot in two worlds, yet you don't completely belong to either. You are living, yet you are also grieving.
You have a child, yet you are child-less.
You are still you, yet you are not who you used to be.
Your life may appear the same on the outside, yet inside everything has changed.
You are a mother, yet you don't have your child to hold.

You are in-between.

In many ways, this in-between is now the world you will forever inhabit. In some ways, we all do whether we've had our baby die or not. Life is always in process and we are ever-shifting beings. It is, however, much more abrupt and in-your-face when your baby dies.

That being said, life won't always feel so unsettled and confusing. You won't always feel like such a sense of non-belonging.

Eventually, you will settle into your new life and your new self and both of those will feel familiar. One day, you'll wake up and feel normal and comfortable in your own skin again. It may not feel the same as it did but it will feel like yours again.

I promise, you will.

In the meantime, let's get familiar and comfortable with the uncertainty and gray of the in-between.

Your Assignment:
Get to Know Your In-Between Self

Settle into your cozy area for some reflection time. Light your candle and make a cup of coffee or tea or cocoa.

Take a chunk of time, or several small bits of time, to consider these questions.

- What pieces of my old self have stayed with me through this experience?
- How have I changed through the experience of the death of my child?
- Are there pieces of how I've changed that I dislike?
- Are there pieces of how I've changed that I can like and appreciate?

- What parts of my old life still remain in this new world called life after loss?
- How has my life changed through this experience of loss?
- Are there parts of this new life that I dislike?
- Are there parts of these life changes that I can like and appreciate?

Take your time reflecting on these questions. Think not just of tangible, observable changes, but also those changes deep inside you and those that can't been seen on the surface.

It can be challenging to look at the positive changes that come out of loss or experiences like the death of someone we love so deeply. Sometimes, we feel guilty for feeling anything positive around devastating losses like those of our children. When our grief is fresh, it can be difficult to see or find anything positive.

It's okay to take this slowly. You have as much time as you need. But please don't avoid those questions or gloss over them. Percolate on them for a while and let it be ok for whatever comes to come. If anger comes, let anger be ok. If sadness comes, be sad. If you feel relief, allow for the relief. Whatever you feel, let it be what it is.

There are no right or wrong answers for this. And if you reflect on these again in a month or a year or 5 years, your answers may be vastly different. It's all part of the in-between process.

Whatever comes is perfect and right.

As always, bring whatever you wish to the Facebook group and let us be there with you.

Your Assignment:
Get to Know Your In-Between Self

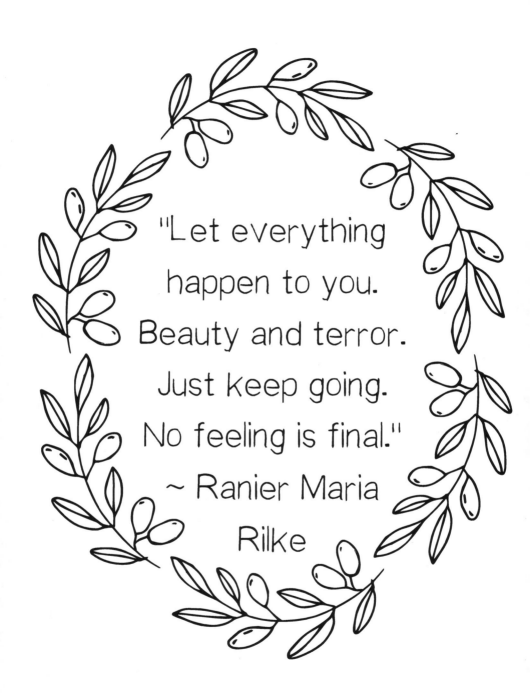

"Let everything happen to you. Beauty and terror. Just keep going. No feeling is final." ~ Ranier Maria Rilke

Part of me wishes I could make this book and this process somehow more fun and light-hearted for you. Unfortunately, doing this kind of healing work isn't easy or comfortable. It's challenging, deep, and, at times, emotionally raw.

What no one likes to tell us about healing is that healing hurts like hell.

The death of our babies demolishes everything we thought we knew about life and ourselves.

However, contrary to popular belief, it doesn't magically make us stronger, kinder, and more evolved people. Loss simply gives us the **chance** to be more than we were and to create a deeper meaning for our lives than we may have previously desired.

The truth is that we decide how this experience is going to define us. We decide who we want to be out of this unimaginable loss. Loss doesn't have to define who we are. We do have a choice in who we become through our experience of loss.

We could drown in the darkness and the sorrow for the rest of our lives. Or we can choose to crawl our way out of the pit of grief and loss. We could rage and rail against the unfairness of having had to say good-bye to our babies forever. Or we can choose to focus on remembering and honoring the life and gifts that they were.

We get to decide:
Are we going to be a bereaved mother?
Or are we going to be a mother who also happens to be bereaved?

The distinction might seem slight, but it is vitally important.

This work of redefining ourselves and our life is hard work. It takes time and intention and commitment. And it takes a willingness to allow some light into the darkness.

That's what we're doing today.

Your Assignment:
Letting In a Glimmer of Light

There are 3 pieces to this assignment – and it's an assignment that will continue throughout this course and, hopefully, long after.

The first is a daily gratitude practice.

Spent a few moments every day – perhaps right before you go to bed each night – and find 3-5 things you are grateful for from that day.

They don't have to be big things. In fact, small is great. Nor do they have to be deep or profound things. Simple is often best.

You could simply be grateful for coffee. Or chocolate. Or the love of your pet. Or for the sunshine. Or the warmth of a hug from your partner or a friend.

Some days all you may be able to come up with is that you were able to open your eyes, you managed to eat some sort of vegetable, and that you have a roof over your head.

What specifically you are grateful for isn't important. What is important is engaging in the daily practice of actively looking for something to be grateful for each day.

It's like looking for glimmers of starlight in the dark of night – pinpoints of light into a world darkened by grief and sorrow and emptiness.

And the more you do it, the brighter those lights become. Gratitude invites light into grief.

Next is the practice of "Just This."

Most of the time, the pain and suffering we feel comes from a resistance to what is happening in our world in the moment – and the longing for what isn't.

Honestly, mindfulness and anything "meditation-ish" are not my strengths. My brain prefers to go a million miles an hour in every direction except here and now. I often struggle with this practice.

However, I keep working on it because I've learned that practicing focusing on "just this," whatever **this** happens to be, is hugely helpful in reducing the amount of suffering I feel at any given moment.

In terms of grief, it means allowing whatever is there to simply be ok and to be there without trying to change it.

Feeling sad? Be sad.
Feeling angry? Be angry.
Having fun? Have fun.
Feeling empty? Feel empty.
Feeling silly? Be silly.
Feeling annoyed? Be annoyed.

Let it be until you are feeling something else.

Honestly, most feelings we experience wouldn't last half as long if we would stop resisting them. They'd come and they'd move through much more easily if there was nothing fighting them.

Fighting our feelings or making ourselves wrong for feeling them is what keeps them around longer.

So, whatever you are feeling or doing, allow yourself to feel or do "just this."

And, finally, let's look at your little delights.

Now, I know that in the intensity and depth of grief, nothing really feels delightful. Mostly, it feels like everything is gray and blah and numb – except for when it feels awful.

However, delight will return again and it's important to reach for it.

I've found that when dealing with the rawness grief and loss, joy feels WAY out of reach. It feels huge and unattainable and unrealistic. Especially if our baby's death was recent.

When people encouraged me to look for joy and happiness in the first few years of my grief, my internal (and occasionally external) response was something like, "Fuck joy." (And fuck you, too.)

Delight on the other hand, felt more attainable to me. It felt more possible. It felt simpler and way less exhausting.

So, make a list of things that delight you. Simple things, small things.

Candles.
Flowers.
Sunrises.
Kitty snuggles.
Fresh picked raspberries.
Hugs.
Hot cocoa.
Walks in the woods or on the beach.
A funny movie.
A good book.
Going for a run.
Scooby-Doo cartoons.
Waffles.

Those are a few of mine. Don't overthink it. Look for little things that you could incorporate into your life on a regular basis without too much extra effort.

Then make a list of at least 30. Keep it on hand for those moments when everything feels overwhelming or stressful. Carry it with you, post it on your fridge or bathroom mirror, tape it in your car. Have it handy when you need some delight.

These are simple, basic practices. They would do all of us some good even if we weren't dealing with this painful loss of our babies.

They are glimmers of light in the darkness of grief. It's okay to seek them.

When you've had some time to get started on these, bring your delights and your gratitude to the group! We're here for the good stuff as well as the hard.

Your Assignment: Letting In a Glimmer of Light

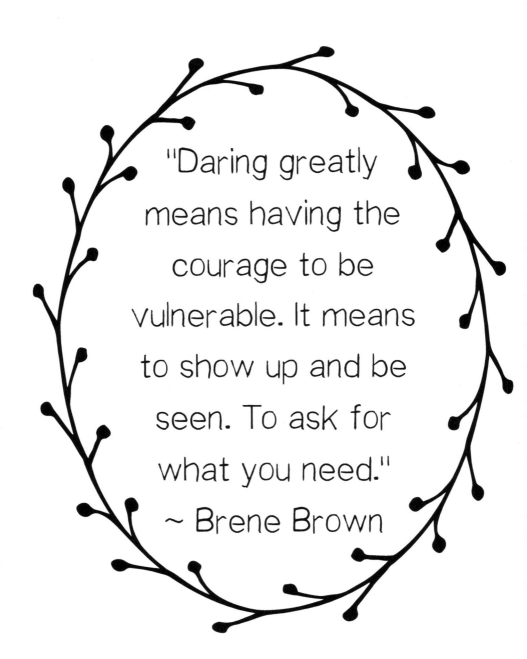

"Daring greatly
means having the
courage to be
vulnerable. It means
to show up and be
seen. To ask for
what you need."
~ Brene Brown

No one can walk this journey of grief but you.

It sucks, but it's the truth.

People can walk beside you. They can walk ahead of you to show possible paths. They can follow behind you as they're finding their own path. They can abandon your path altogether and be nowhere in sight. They can pop in and out randomly at different places along the path. Their path may run parallel to yours for a while. They can give you a map that may or may not be useful to you.

But no one can do your walking except for you.

One of the hardest parts of any grief journey, in my opinion, is how lonely the journey can feel. To some degree that sense of loneliness is simply an unavoidable part of the process.

Our relationship with our baby is unique and irreplaceable. No one else, even our partners or closest family members, had the same relationship with our babies as we did. As a result, no one can truly understand or know our specific and unique experience of loss. Nor can we fully understand their relationship with our baby or their experience of loss.

That's why much of this journey feels so very lonely. Accepting that this is our journey alone and letting go of expecting our family and friends to understand our experience is painful and challenging.

And it's vitally important to moving forward.

That is not to say, however, that we have to walk alone.

While our relationship with our baby and with our grief is singularly unique and no one can do this journey FOR us, there are those who can be WITH us.

In my experience, the biggest obstacle to navigating the in-between and finding a way to embrace our new selves and our new life is not knowing how to ask for or receive the support we need.

So, before we move toward the actual redefining portion of this course, let's look at how you're feeling about your level of support + how to ask for and receive said support.

The truth is, most of us aren't very good at asking for or receiving support. I know I'm not. That's not to say that we don't want it – most of us desperately do.

The trouble is that it is often easy to fall into the trap of expecting others to know what we want or need without us having to tell them or ask for it. We want them to just magically **know** what we need and give it to us because, to us, it feels like it should be obvious what we need. It's not obvious – not to those not living our unique experience. Unfortunately, though it could be easier at times for us, people aren't mind readers.

We're in unimaginable pain and we don't want to have to ask for what we need. Half the time, we aren't even sure what we need.

Except really we do know what we need. We may not know how to ask or we might feel uncomfortable or afraid of asking for what we need, but generally speaking, we know.

It annoys the hell out of me, but usually when I tell myself I don't know what I want or need, it's because I don't like the answer I'm getting. Dammit.

It takes courage and vulnerability to ask for what we need and to let someone give it to us. It's a very uncomfortable space and the answer might be no. We have to accept the no's.

It could also be yes. We have to accept those too.

Learning to ask for and receive support also requires some discernment in knowing who can be trusted with your vulnerability and heart. Asking someone for support who has repeatedly shown you that they aren't, for whatever reason, able to give you that support is like punching yourself in the face.

Don't do that! Seriously. If people have shown you in the past that they can't be there for you, don't reach out to them. Expecting them to change and being repeatedly disappointed when they don't is only going to hurt you. When someone has shown you what they can or cannot offer you, believe them.

Instead, let's explore who *are* your safe and trusted people.

Your Assignment
Find Your Sources of Support

Identify your peeps.

Who can you go to when you are crying and overwhelmed with grief?
Who can you go to for practical stuff – when your brain is just too overwhelmed to make sense of simple instructions or directions?
Who can you ask for help when you just can't deal with facing crowds or people yet you need groceries and tampons?
Who can you call on when you just need some distraction and someone to make you smile or laugh a little?

It might be that one or two people might be able to provide all of this for you. Or you might have different people for each different need.

Think about what you need and take a look at those people, in-person, distant, and online, who can be there in the way that you need. Make lists and keep them handy for those moments when you need them.

And be prepared to adjust your lists as you continue to learn who can and cannot be there for you. These lists of supporters will change and shift throughout life.

You deserve love and support on every step of this journey. You have to walk it for yourself, but we're all in this together – you don't have to walk alone.

And, as always, bring any challenges and difficulties to the group. Let us support you. (And take note of whether you've utilized this support option yet. . .if not, why not?)

Are you ready to let yourself be loved, exactly as and where you are?

Your Assignment: Find Your Sources of Support

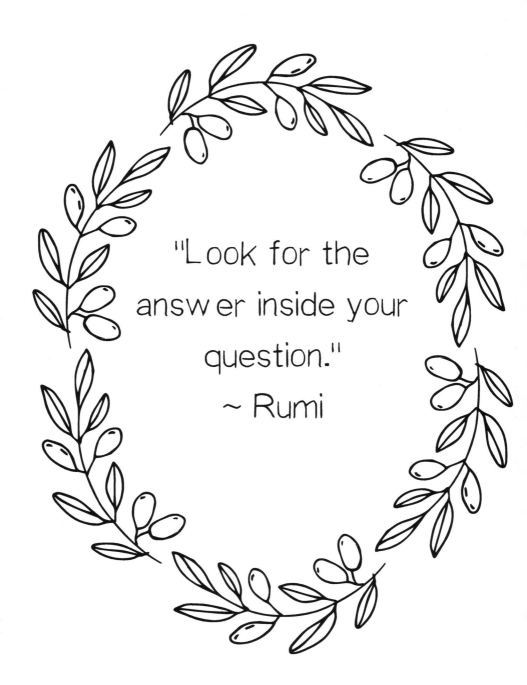

"Look for the answer inside your question."
~ Rumi

Your baby died.

It is a horrible, painful, unfair, and unimaginable truth.

Yet you are still here.

You are still standing. You are still breathing. You are still living.

It's time to start considering and choosing how you want to live and be in this life that you still have. No, it's not the life you planned or the life you wanted, but it's still life and it's still yours.

It's easy after such an immense loss to drift through life or to fight your way through the mess of it.

All of that is natural and normal, especially in the first few years after your baby dies. Grieving consumes your life for a while and it cannot be avoided (not in a way that's helpful in the long-term at least).

But you deserve more than drifting or fighting through life. You will grieve in different ways and different times throughout your lifetime, but grieving doesn't have to consume your life forever.

Beginning to truly *live while grieving rather than grief being your life* means making some conscious choices about who you want to be, what kind of a mother you want to be (whether or not you have living children), and what kind of a life you want to live with the circumstances you've been given.

Choose what you want for yourself and take back your life.

It's not easy. This thing called living after loss comes with it's own set of scars and battles and fierceness.

At first it's about simple survival. Now, however, it becomes about learning to embrace the challenges of not just surviving, but also living and laughing and thriving.

Let's get started, shall we?

Your Assignment:
Redefining Motherhood and Yourself

You've spent time saying good-bye. Now, let's start to say hello.

This assignment will focus on you and your motherhood, on who you want to be now and what you want your motherhood to look like in the circumstances you have been given. Next time, we'll talk about redefining life as a whole.

The first part of this assignment is to redefine your motherhood.

The painful truth is that we don't get to be the kind of mothers we expected to be – to hold, feed, nurture, teach, tend, and love in the physical. We don't get to nurse or soothe our babies, we don't get to watch them grow or teach them to walk or talk, we don't get to see them hit milestones and make friends and become independent. Our babies are forever still and forever gone.

Since we can't be the kind of mother we thought we'd be, what kind of mother do we want to be *now*?

Our babies might not be here in physical form, but we are still mothers.

How that looks in our life now is up to us.

Some questions to ponder and explore in your journal:

- How do I define motherhood?
- How has my definition of motherhood changed?
- What kind of mother do I want to be to my baby?
- What does it look like to mother my baby?
- What does it feel like to mother my baby?

- How would I mother my baby if I didn't care what anyone else thought about it?

And then, perhaps most importantly, *what can I do to mother my baby right now?*

The second part of this assignment is about you as an individual.

You are a mother and that is likely a vital aspect of who you are, however, you are also *more* than a mother.

We've talked quite a bit about how you aren't the same you that existed before your baby died. You didn't have much choice in that transformation, you were you and then you became a different you.

Now it's time to choose who you **want** to be going forward.

- What kind of person do you want to be?
- How do you want to feel? About yourself? About life?
- What kind of partner/daughter/friend/sister/etc do you want to be?
- How do you want to experience life?
- If you were this person you imagine, what would you be doing differently? How would you be thinking, acting, talking, being different than you are right now?

Sometimes it's hard to imagine that it's possible to feel good about life and ourselves again after this kind of all-encompassing loss.

One of my favorite little practices for getting a glimpse of who I could become is to write a letter to myself – from my future self. I imagine myself 5, 10, 30 years from now, writing a letter of comfort and encouragement and love to the me of now.

Who are you 5 or 10 or 30 years from now? What would she want you to know? What would she say to you?

Let that future you write you a letter and see what she has to say. Have fun with it! And, then, as always, feel free to bring it to the group and share your insights.

Always remember, this is a process. You won't have all the answers today. That's okay. It's all one step at a time.

Your Assignment: Redefining Motherhood and Yourself

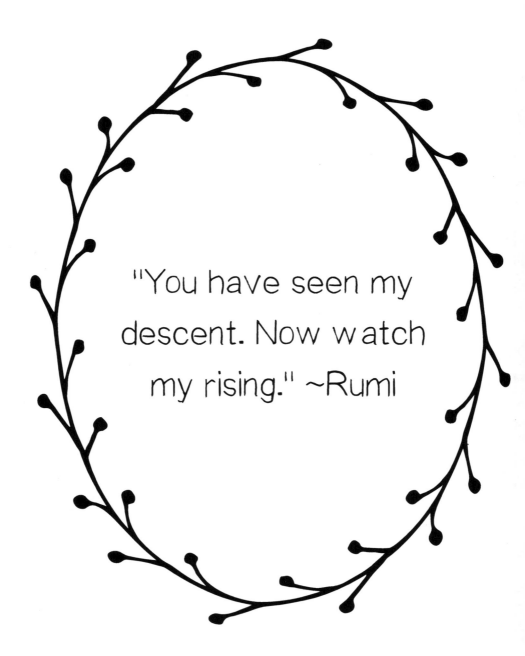

"You have seen my descent. Now watch my rising." ~Rumi

There are so many things in life that we cannot control.

Losing our babies was one of them.

However, we do have a choice in deciding what we want to do with the life we are handed after the loss of our baby. We have a choice in deciding who we want to become as individuals, as mothers, and as women because of or in spite of the painful death of our babies.

We can be defined by this loss. We can let it rule our life.

Or, we make the choice to define life, motherhood, and ourselves for ourselves. We can decide what meaning we want to make out of life and out of this loss.

Nothing and no one gets to do that for us. Not life. Not this experience. Not the world we live in. Not anyone around us.

We get to decide. We can't change what did happen. We can't know for sure what will come next in life.

We can decide what it means to us now and how we want to move forward in it.

This doesn't mean that we forget about our babies or our loss. It doesn't mean we "find closure" or "move on" or "find the reason for it." There is no closure to life (not even death). Moving forward is very different from forgetting or pretending it never happened. And making meaning out of an experience is very different from blindly declaring that must have been a reason for it. Those statements are baseless clique statements created by people too uncomfortable with the depths of life to face them head on.

That's not what we are about here. By the simple fact that you chose to purchase this journal, you have proven you are willing to face this painful experience and all that comes after head on.

Grief and the death of our baby brings us to our knees. It decimates the foundation underneath us and turns life as we knew it inside out.

Making meaning out of that experience is how we reclaim life for ourselves. It's how we take back our own individual power and learn to not just stand, but to walk, run, dance, and laugh again.

And, yes, feeling joy and happiness and being able to walk, run, dance, and laugh again is possible, even after this, the most devastating and painful of losses.

And, yes, as so many mothers ask, you can even find a sense of purpose in life again. That's a core piece of what meaning making is all about. As Viktor Frankl put it in <u>A Man's Search for Meaning</u>, *"Any person, regardless of the circumstances, can decide what shall become of them – mentally and spiritually."*

Life has handed you the most painful and unbearable of circumstances – the death of your baby.

Now, you get to decide what shall become of you.

Your Assignment:
Embracing a New Life and New Meaning

One of the turning points in my journey called life after loss was when I started asking myself this question:

"What will I do with the life I have now?"

I couldn't change what happened to my daughters. I couldn't go back in time and reclaim the life I once had. I couldn't be who I used to be. I couldn't predict what life would hold in the future.

So, I started to ask myself, "what do I want to do with the life I have now?"

What do you want to do with the life you have now?

Take this journal and settle into your space to consider that question. If you can look past the anger, the grief, the unfairness of not having the life you wanted to have - ***what do you want to do with the life you have now?***

What purpose do you want for it?

I think sometimes we get caught in this idea that our purpose in life is somehow bestowed upon us at birth and we just have to discover it.

That's a bunch of bullshit.

You decide what purpose your life has and will have. You get to decide what you want to do with it and what meaning you want to give it.

Maybe that purpose has to do with this experience and the child you lost. Or maybe that purpose has nothing to do with this experience and the child you lost.

There is no right or wrong purpose to have for your life.

And, once you've sat with that question for a while and explored what has come up, take it to another level.

What legacy do you want to live and to leave behind?

That legacy can be big and grand or simple and sweet.

Perhaps you decide to build an empire and be a well-known figure in your professional field. Perhaps you decide you want to leave a legacy in which every person who knew you felt loved and valued. Perhaps you decide you want to simply live in a state of gratitude throughout your life and reflect that in your actions.

The specifics aren't important – as long as it feels right and meaningful to you.

It's your legacy and your life.

What do you want to do with it now?

Come share your thoughts, dreams, realizations, and everything in between in the Facebook group! Let us support you.

Your Assignment:
Embracing a New Life and New Meaning

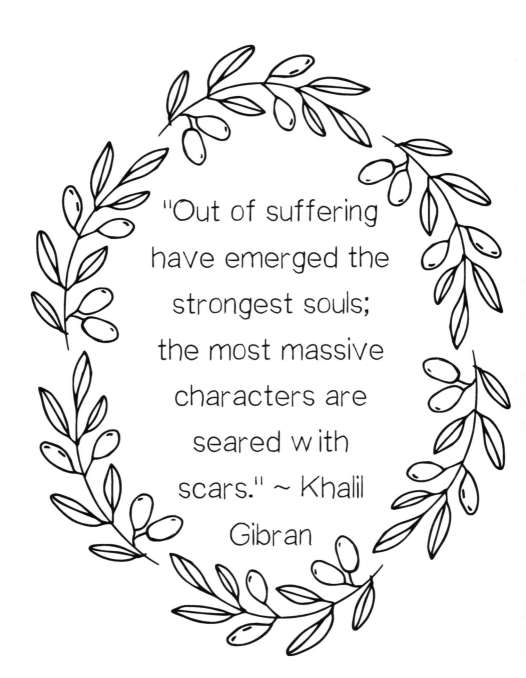

"Out of suffering have emerged the strongest souls; the most massive characters are seared with scars." ~ Khalil Gibran

After having spent some time exploring your answers to "what do I want to do with the life I have now" and "what legacy do I want to leave behind" and "who do I want to be now" and "what kind of mother do I want to be now" it's time to move into living those answers.

This is the final "to-do" step in this book, but it's just the beginning for you and the beautiful life ahead of you.

When we lose our child, life on the outside appears as if nothing has changed to those looking in. They can't see the massive, yawning hole we are left with. We, of course, know that nothing is the same. We feel that gaping hole every day.

We've spent most of this course saying good-bye to our former life and selves as well as getting familiar with the unsettled and painful in-between. We're not done with either of those things. We may never be fully done with those things. All of this is an ever-evolving life-long process.

We will forever be creating and re-creating our lives, ourselves, and our motherhood, whether it's forced upon us by the loss of someone we deeply love or by the day-to-day progression of life.

To create our lives mindfully and consciously, we will ask ourselves the questions in the previous pages of this book again and again throughout our lives.

Now, however, it's time to consciously move forward in creating that beautiful life. It's time to put desires and thoughts of who you want to be and what you want your life to look like into action.

Your Assignment
Creating the New

Let's take a look at how closely your current experience of life, motherhood, and yourself matches the one you've imagined and created in your mind throughout the last few weeks.

Pull out your favorite pens or markers or colored pencils and settle into your cozy spot.

We're going to make a list. I'm a big fan of list-making! However, if you're like a dear friend of mine and lists bring about a sense of panic, feel free to draw or use another method for this assignment – make this practice your own.

First, I want you to create 3 lists (or the equivalent) of all the qualities, feelings, ideas, experiences, etc. of :

a) the life
b) the motherhood
c) the you

that you have created and imagined over the course of this journaling process.

Be specific.

How does life feel?
What sort of activities do you do as a mother?
What habits do you have as the new you?
What kind of friends do you have as the new you in your new life?
How is your baby present in your new life?
What brings you pleasure now?
What kind of fun things do you do?
How do you eat? Sleep? Exercise?
What kind of work do you do?
What do your relationships look like?
How do you feel about your body?
What do your routines look like?
What matters to you?
What doesn't matter to you?

Nothing is too trivial or too large for these lists. They should be rather long and descriptive.

Once you have these lists, I want you to go through them and create a list from them of all the things on them that are NOT currently present in your life experience. Then write a list of the things that ARE currently present.

It could be that you are already engaging in many of the activities and feelings on your original lists. Or it could be that your current life looks nothing like the life you want to create. Either is totally fine!

We all start from somewhere. And this is where the real work begins.

It's time to start living those unique to you life/motherhood/me-I-want-to-be lists. One small piece at a time.

Pick something from one of those lists and decide to start living or being that.

Maybe it's taking a 10-minute walk every day. Maybe it's calling a friend to go to a movie. Maybe it's sending a card to a loved one. Maybe it's volunteering. Maybe it's writing a blog about your experience of grief and loss. Maybe it's looking for a different career or looking at schools to go back to. Maybe it's taking 30 minutes every day to do something you love but never give yourself time for.

Again, the specific what isn't important – it just has to matter to you.

It'll be different for everyone. And you don't have to do it all at once.

As I've said, this is a process that will evolve and unfold over months and years and your entire lifetime.

The death of your baby took away the life, motherhood, and you that you had planned and expected to be.

You deserve to reclaim your life and to shape it how you want it to be now, even if it can't be what you wanted and will always be missing an essential person.

As you get started, come on over to the group and share how you're doing and where you are starting!

Your Assignment: Creating the New

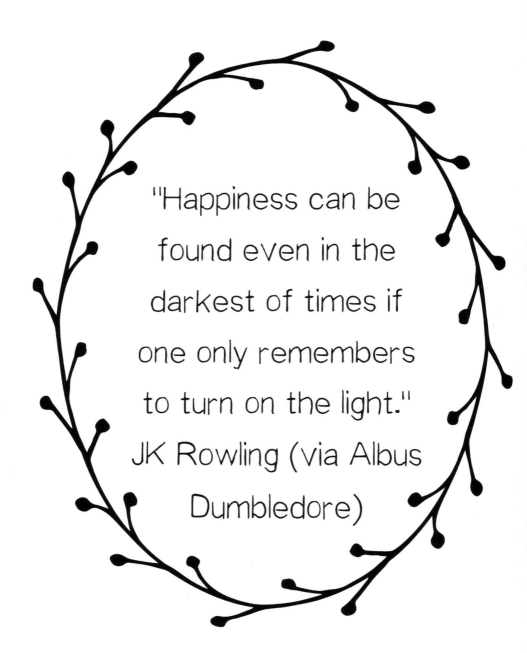

"Happiness can be found even in the darkest of times if one only remembers to turn on the light." JK Rowling (via Albus Dumbledore)

We've arrived at the end of this journal. But it's not the end.

Life is ever-evolving. The you that you are creating now will not be the you that will exist 5 years from now. Even if life is nothing but kind and gentle and sweet to you, in 5 years you will be a different you and a different mother living a different life.

That's what life is - an ever changing and ever unfolding process of living.

You will never be done re-creating yourself or your life or your motherhood. And that's ok.

If needed, you have this journal and these practices to reference when life takes a turn on you, as it will in many different ways over the years. You can pick up this journal again and work your way through it as many times as you need to over the years.

You will also have the Facebook group for as long as Facebook exists and I am doing this work. You are always welcome there for support and encouragement – or to offer your support and wisdom to others who might be just starting this journey.

We all learn from each other. We all grow together. Our journey together may have started in this journal, but it doesn't have to end there.

I am grateful for this time with you and for your trust in me to share what I have learned and what support I can offer. I can promise that I've learned as much from you and this journal as you have from it and me.

We're all in this together.

I am so grateful we don't have to do it alone.

Made in the USA
Middletown, DE
17 September 2017